Nyiragitwa

A story by Ndamyumugabe, Jerome Irankunda and Erin Jessee
Illustrations by Christian Mugarura

Published by Mudacumura Publishing House in 2021
Kigali, Rwanda
Kicukiro, Gatenga,
KK46 Ave1
Website: www.mudacumurapublishing.com
Email: mudacumurapublishing@gmail.com
P.O. Box: 4074 Kigali

Foreword

In Rwanda, the act of narrating Rwanda's past is never a solitary endeavor, and this graphic novel is no different. Before the introduction of written language in Rwanda, oral traditions were passed down from one generation to the next by Rwandans who often served the monarchy as court ritualists and were carefully training in the art of storytelling and the history of the kingdom of Rwanda and its neighbors.

The particular story underlying this graphic novel, Nyiragitwa: Daughter of Sacyega, was inherited by one such Rwandan known to us only as Ndamyumugabe. He told it to the Belgian historian, Jan Vansina, and an unnamed Rwandan research assistant in 1958. The recording was then carefully transcribed by the research assistant in Kinyarwanda and translated into French.

The resulting transcripts were then unearthed in 2010 by American historian Sarah E. Watkins, during her archival research on Rwandan Queen Mothers. She kindly shared these transcripts with Canadian oral historian, Erin Jessee, to facilitate her Royal Society of Edinburgh-funded project on 'Rwandan social bonds in historical perspective.' This project was made possible with the support of the Rwanda Academy of Language to explore the diverse identities and practices that bonded or divided Rwandans before the twentieth century.

Jerome Irankunda and Erin Jessee translated the original Kinyarwanda transcript of Nyiragitwa into English. They then condensed the story into a format that was more suitable for a short graphic novel. They then worked with graphic novelist Christian Mugarura, who created illustrations to help tell the story in greater detail. We worked together to give him feedback on making the images as culturally and historically appropriate as possible.

This process has altered Ndamyumugabe's original words in various ways, but we hope it has preserved his original meaning as much as possible. Similarly, its historical accuracy is limited by the lack of photographs and other relevant visual aids related to the time period in which Nyiragitwa allegedly lived: during the reign of the seventeenth-century king, Cyirima Rujigira.

We chose to turn this oral tradition into a graphic novel as part of a broader effort to write Rwandan women back into the history of Rwanda. Nyiragitwa is one of several Rwandan women who have emerged from the oral traditions documented by Vansina between 1958 and 1960 – a period of remarkable and, at times, violent, political transformation in Rwanda that immediately preceded the nation's independence in 1962.

To this end, we have chosen to highlight Nyiragitwa's story not because we see her as exceptional, but rather because she exemplifies the many women who – according to Rwandan oral traditions – once exercised significant authority in their communities, but whose contributions have been largely overlooked by historians who specialize in Rwandan history. We hope that this graphic novel will serve as a starting point for writing women back into Rwanda's early history.

Dedicated to Dr. James Vuningoma, 1948-2020. Rest in power.

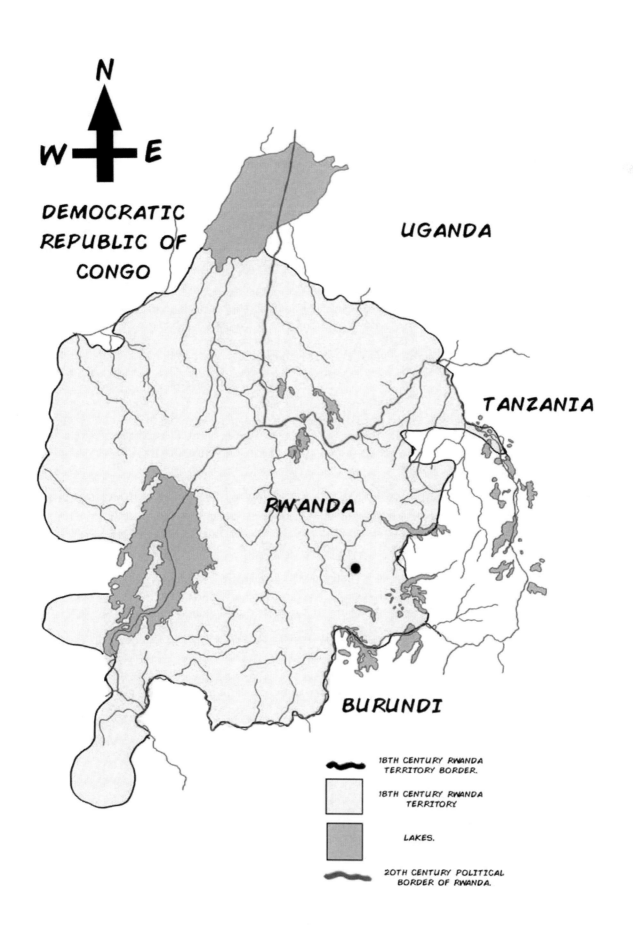

DEMOCRATIC REPUBLIC OF CONGO

UGANDA

TANZANIA

RWANDA

BURUNDI

18TH CENTURY RWANDA TERRITORY BORDER.

18TH CENTURY RWANDA TERRITORY

LAKES.

20TH CENTURY POLITICAL BORDER OF RWANDA.

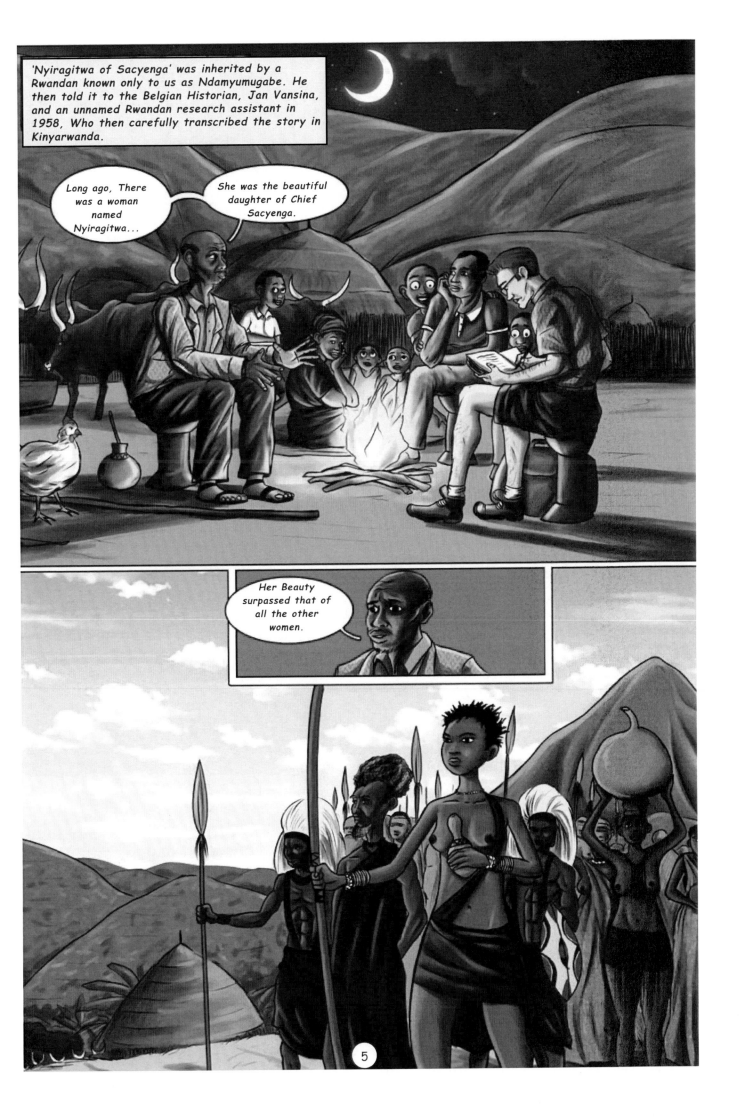

The wealthiest clans from across the kingdom flocked to Sacyega's home.

My compatriots, Thank you for making the long and perilous journey to our humble home...

I'm sure my daughter will find a husband among you.

Please accept my son's proposal on my behalf.

?

I don't want your son for a husband!

!

6

Her father agreed. He built her a beautiful house and gave her ten cattle.

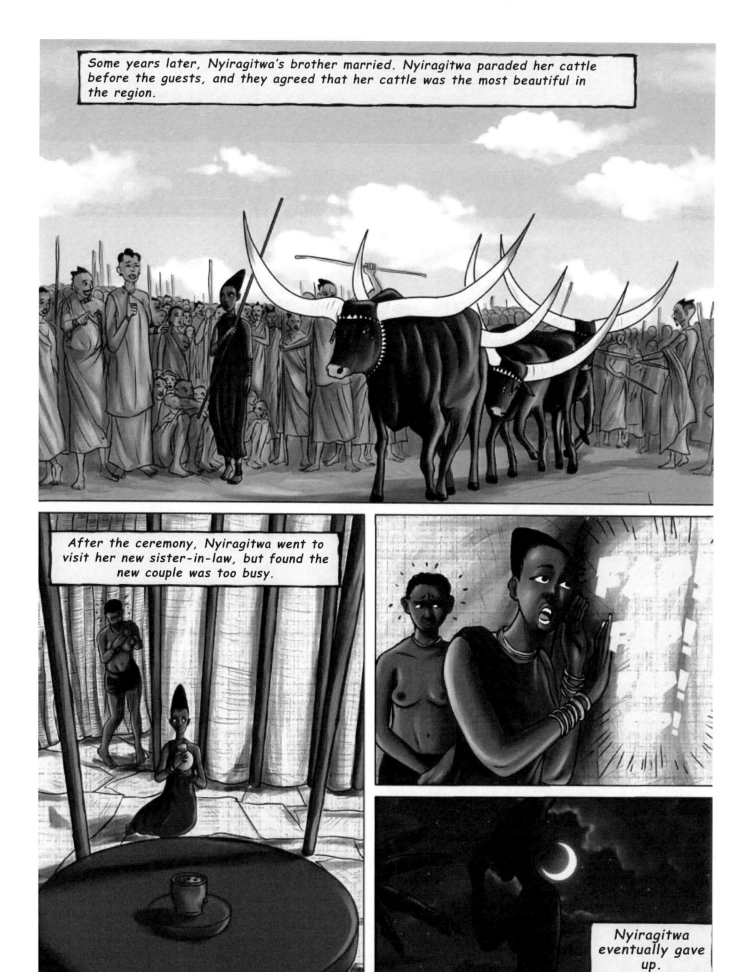

Some years later, Nyiragitwa's brother married. Nyiragitwa paraded her cattle before the guests, and they agreed that her cattle was the most beautiful in the region.

After the ceremony, Nyiragitwa went to visit her new sister-in-law, but found the new couple was too busy.

Nyiragitwa eventually gave up.

She left with a heavy heart.

To raise her spirits, Nyiragitwa took her cattle to a watering hole. There, She found a large herd of beautiful cattle.

And invited their owner, a handsome young man to sit with her.

Let us greet each other.

Nyiragitwa met the young man many times at the watering hole after that.

Visit me so that I can offer you some tobacco.

Impressed by how well he cared for his cattle, Nyiragitwa invited him to her home.

When he arrived, Nyiragitwa's servants served him banana beer, and Tobacco flavored with honey, which he received with gratitude.

No.

Do you have a wife?

When you go home, act very sad and refuse to drink beer or milk. When your father asks you what is wrong, tell him you want to marry Nyiragitwa, daughter of Sacyega, but you fear it is impossible.

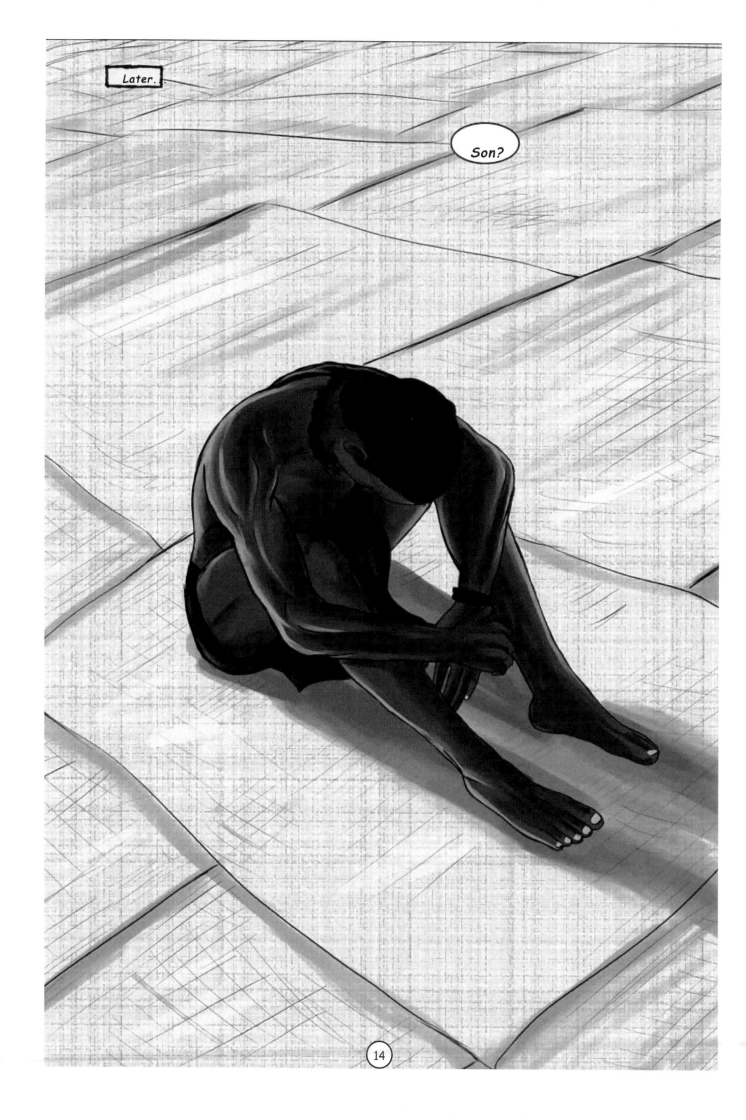

The young man's father went to visit Nyiragitwa.

Please, let's not delay. Tell your son to return in eight days and we will be married.

Okay!

After eight days of preparation...

The young man went to Nyiragitwa's home to marry her.

When the celebrations finished, the boys took their cattle to the watering hole.

Why are you not joining them?

I am no longer a boy!

Nyiragitwa insisted her new husband go with them.

When the boys returned, Nyiragitwa's servants served them beer.

Her husband grew tired, and decided to take his wife to bed.

Be quick about it.

What?

Never mind. Don't come near me again!

I don't want trouble here.

The young man went to complain to Sacyega, but Nyiragitwa's servant had already brought him the news.

Please give me back my father's cattle.

Nyiragitwa says that if you want the cattle back, you should send your father.

When her father-in-law arrived, Nyiragitwa welcomed him.

Isn't this the most beautiful house? Have you ever seen it?

Yes

Yes, Nyiragitwa. Everything you have is beautiful.

Isn't this house the right size? Isn't this pillar strong? Aren't this floor and these mats nicely woven?

Isn't the entrance to my bedroom well made?

Isn't my bed soft?

Aren't the baskets well-placed?

Nyiragatwa had dreamt of his arrival, though. She was ready for him.

You, milking the cow.

Please prepare a fire for our guest.

She had her servants prepare many fine things.

When the brother arrived, He found Nyiragitwa was expecting him.

But each time Nyiragitwa offered him something, the brother rejected it.

Please enjoy some tobacco.

This tobacco is terrible.

Please try this delicious banana beer.

Why would you serve me this?

Perhaps you would enjoy this exellent honey beer more?

Propably not. But i might enjoy you!

The couple did not emerge from Nyiragitwa's house for the rest of the nights.

Meanwhile, a thief heard that Nyiragitwa was distracted.

But the young man saw the thief and killed him.

A man has been killed!

His mother will be ashamed

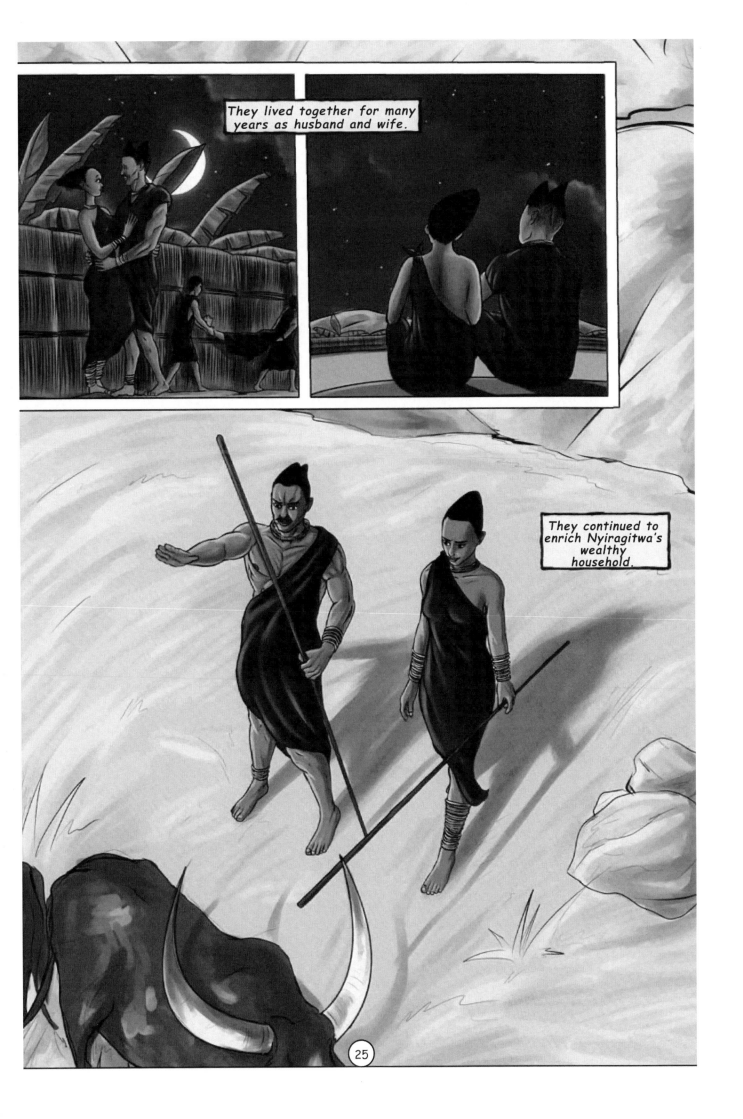

They lived together for many years as husband and wife.

They continued to enrich Nyiragitwa's wealthy household.

Meanwhile, at the edges of the kingdom, the king was fighting a great battle.

The king called for his chiefs to fight with him. And Nyiragitwa's husband agreed.

26

27

But Nyiragitwa's husband was determined and left early the next morning.

Nyiragitwa sought consolation with the other women in her family.

We must prepare for the warriors' return.

We don't know what happens among soldiers. We haven't been to war.

The women began preparing beer to welcome their husbands.

When the warriors returned, all of Nyiragitwa's predictions proved true.

But Nyiragitwa's mother-in-law remained troubled by Nyiragitwa's visions.

She is a sorceress! She predicted that you would be wounded, and that our idiot son-in-law would bring home a blind cow. She has a bad heart.

If you love me and believe I have raised good children, you must force Nyiragitwa to leave.

I will speak to her.

Nyiragitwa's father-in-law invited everyone to drink together.

Nyiragitwa, I have heard that you predicted what would happen to us, warriors. Why didn't you tell me?

32

Yes, it's true. But I don't have a bad heart.

I rejected my first husband because he did not love cattle. And I could not love a man who did not love cattle.

And I knew my father-in-law would then come to my home and try to make me one of his wives.

Perhaps the wound to his thigh was punishment for trying to seduce me. But I was not the one who wounded him.

And it's true I had a vision about how our warriors would fare in battle.

I saw my brother-in-law panicking and rushing to loot stupid things that he could carry easily. Even when cattle were all around him.

But it is my love for my husband that made this possible. I have seen how he loves cattle and remains vigilant against our enemies. Even when he is sleeping.

I see no evidence of Nyiragitwa's wrongdoing. I give Nyiragitwa authority over all of my children. And should anyone cause you trouble, you may take their possessions as punishment.

This is how Nyiragitwa became very famous, powerful and chief in her own right.

The couple lived happily ever after.

THE END.

35

Mudacumura Publishing House